Copyrigh

All rights reserved. No part of this publication maybe reproduced, distributed, or transmitted in any form or by any means, including photocopying, recording, or other electronic or mechanical methods, without the prior written permission of the publisher, except in the case of brief quotations embodied in critical reviews and certain other noncommercial uses permitted by copyright law.

Contents

What Is Pureed Diet?

Chewing and swallowing regular foods safely and efficiently requires a certain level of strength and coordination. Many things can go wrong that affect the swallowing process, for instance a stroke, Parkinson’s disease, certain types of dementia, ALS (amyotrophic lateral sclerosis or Lou Gherig’s disease), and head or neck cancer.

A puréed diet is needed for people with chewing and swallowing difficulties. The diet is a texture-amended diet in which all foods have a soft, pudding-like uniformity. This diet is often recommended for people who can't eat solid foods because of a health concern or injury that prevents normal chewing or digestion.

The goal of a puréed diet is to provide a variety of foods that meet your nutritional needs to help you heal and prevent any degree of malnutrition. Compared to a liquid diet, a puréed diet provides more variety, nutrients, and fiber. That means it's safe to stay on it for longer than a liquid diet.

When is pureed food recommended?

Sometimes a person has a high risk of choking or aspirating normal solid foods into the lungs, or is at risk of malnutrition because they struggle so much to eat. Often, in these case, the person can manage to eat pureed foods with minimal risk.

Pureed foods don't require chewing and aren't as likely to remain in the mouth or throat after swallowing.

But pureed foods aren't always safe in every situation, so it's important that anyone with difficulty swallowing see a speech-language pathologist for an evaluation.

Pureed Food for Swallowing Problems

For individuals with swallowing problems, making sure the food is the right consistency is important. Pureed fruits and vegetables, milkshakes, pudding, and soups are examples of pureed foods for swallowing problems.

A Speech Therapist is often involved with making recommendations for texture modification recommendations. A dietitian is involved with providing diet education and supporting individuals in preparing the appropriate foods.

Pureed Food for Chewing Problems

Individuals with missing teeth, pain in their mouth, or those recovering from an oral procedure may benefit from a pureed diet. Pureed food benefits individuals with chewing problems since these foods require no chewing. High calorie drinks are also beneficial for those who cannot chew for a short period (ex. after tooth removal or oral surgery).

Benefits

Because puréed foods don't have to be chewed, they're easier to swallow and digest. It can act as a bridge between a liquid diet and your normal diet as you recover from an illness or surgery, helping prevent weight loss and maintain your health until you're able to eat normally.

It can also be a long-term solution if, for any number of reasons, you cannot tolerate or manage eating solid foods.

Some of the more common reasons for using a puréed diet include:

- Oral or dental surgery
- Jaw injury or surgery
- Difficulty eating or swallowing problems (dysphagia) caused by a stroke or degenerative neurological diseases such as Parkinson's

disease, Alzheimer's disease, and amyotrophic lateral sclerosis (ALS)5

- Some digestive disorders
- Infection, injury, or ulceration of the mouth, throat, or esophagus
- Head or neck radiation treatment
- Bariatric surgery used to treat obesity6
- Feeding of older adults, especially those with poor teeth or dementia

Proper nutrition is important to maintain good health at all ages. If you've recently had surgery or have an injury to your mouth and can't eat a regular diet, the nutrients you get from a puréed diet are particularly important in your recovery.

Research on the role of nutrition in patients with mouth surgery shows that poor nutrition can delay wound healing, increase your risk of infection, and even compromise your immune system. All forms of texture-modified diets, including a puréed diet, can help prevent complications associated with poor nutrition.

How Does The Diet Work?

Most foods can be puréed, as long as they're cooked properly and you have a good blender or food processor. That means you should still be able to eat most of the foods that you enjoy, though some puréed foods may be more palatable than others.

Foods like pudding or yogurt, which are already the appropriate consistency for this diet, and good choices. The food just has to be soft enough, not necessarily puréed.

Duration

In most cases, a puréed diet is followed for a short period until you are able to chew and digest solid foods normally. You should stay on a puréed diet until your healthcare provider gives you the all-clear to advance to a soft diet or a regular diet.

If your doctor advises you to stick with a puréed diet long term, it is likely, above all, for safety reasons (e.g., to reduce your risk of choking when eating). It's important that you follow these instructions.

What to Eat

Foods To Eat

- Fruits: Any cooked and puréed; juices or nectar without pulp; applesauce

- Vegetables: Any cooked and puréed; whipped mashed or sweet potatoes; vegetable juices without pulp

- Grains: Puréed pasta or rice; cream of wheat/rice cereal; hominy; puréed oatmeal

- Dairy: Milk; smooth yogurts without fruit chunks; puréed cottage cheese; ice cream or frozen yogurt; custard or pudding; whipped cream

- Meats, fish and eggs: Any cooked meats, fish or eggs puréed with liquid, gravy or sauce

- Legumes: Smooth bean dips or hummus; silken or puréed tofu
- Fats: Olive oil; butter; puréed avocado; gravy; sour cream
- Soups
- Desserts: Gelatin; popsicles; fruit ice; smoothies or frappes
- Liquid meal replacement drinks or supplements
- Herbs, spices, or smooth/liquid seasonings (e.g., ketchup, barbecue sauce, mustard)
- Any beverages

Foods To Avoid

- Fruits: Any whole or soft cooked fruits that must be chewed

- Vegetables: Any whole or soft cooked vegetables that must be chewed
- Grains: All other grains that can't be puréed smooth
- Dairy: Yogurt with fruit chunks, or mix-in items; solid cheese; cottage cheese
- Meats, fish, and other proteins: Very tough cuts of meat that can't be puréed smooth; hard boiled or scrambled eggs
- Nuts and seeds: All solid nuts, seeds, and coconut
- Legumes: Baked beans; any cooked legumes that must be chewed; tempeh; baked tofu
- Desserts: Any others that must be chewed

- Condiments with solids (e.g., relish, jam, salsa)

The puréed diet can offer a good deal of variety, but you may find that certain foods are easier to purée or blend smoothly than others. Each type of food needs a different approach.

Fruits

All fruits will soften when cooked, but it will be easier to achieve a smoother consistency if you peel fruits with skins (like apples) first. Before you eat fruits with seeds, like berries, or any fruits with tough membranes, like oranges or grapefruit, make sure you press them through a sieve to remove any solids.

Smooth applesauce or puréed fruit packets are convenient for when you want a quick snack without cooking and blending.

Vegetables

Make sure you peel any vegetables with tough skins and always press vegetables with seeds or "strings" through a sieve before eating.

Vegetable baby food, sold in jars or squeezable packets, can be convenient to have on hand, but make sure you purchase products specifically for babies, as those for toddlers tend to be thicker and/or chunkier.

Dairy

If you need additional calories, choose full-fat dairy products like whole milk or yogurt. Greek yogurt provides about 20 grams of protein in a

6-ounce serving, so it's a good way to boost your intake of this important nutrient.

Meats and Fish

Softer meats like chicken, fish, and ground meats will be easiest to purée. You can add gravy, stock, or a cream sauce to make them smoother. Make sure you press meats or fish through a sieve to remove any solid pieces.

Legumes

All legumes are high in fiber and protein. In addition, they purée very easily. Silken tofu is very soft and makes a good base for creamy desserts or soups. Peanut butter (or other nut butters) is smooth enough to include on a puréed diet, but use caution with if you have any swallowing problems, given its thickness.

Liquid Meal Replacements

Try to keep products like Ensure, Carnation Instant Breakfast, or Boost available for times when you may not feel like cooking, or you have to be away from home.

Another easy homemade and nutritious meal replacement is a smoothie. Just mix milk, water, or juice with any fruit, leafy greens, a scoop of protein powder, and a spoonful of peanut butter or avocado, and you'll have a complete meal.

Herbs and Spices

In general, these are fine to use. However, use caution with cayenne pepper and other hot spices or condiments if you have mouth or tongue sores, as these can be irritating.

What exactly is pureed food?

Pureed food, as quoted from this patient handout from IDDSI (the International Dysphagia Diet Standardization Initiative):

- Is usually eaten with a spoon.
- Does not require chewing.
- Has a smooth texture with no lumps.
- Holds shape on a spoon.
- Falls off a spoon in a single spoonful when tilted.
- Is not sticky.
- Liquid (like sauces) must not separate from solids.

IDDSI emphases that it really comes down to how the food is prepared. So for example, mashed potatoes may be not be a true puree because they could be lumpy or sticky.

But since we all like examples, here are examples of commonly-pureed food. Just be sure the results pass the criteria above!

- Mashed potatoes.
- Souffles.
- Cream of Wheat (farina) cereal.
- Pudding.
- Applesauce.
- Yogurt.
- Ice cream.

Which foods can be pureed?

Any food that isn't hard or has seeds are good candidates. What's critical is that the resulting puree fits the definition above.

- Cooked meats, fish, and chicken.
- Dairy products such as cottage cheese, yogurt, and ice cream.
- Cooked vegetables such as potatoes and beans.
- Canned fruits.
- Ripe bananas and avocados.

You can also puree:

- Soup.
- Eggs.

- Cooked pasta.
- Bread, muffins, and pancakes.
- Fresh ripe fruits without skin or seeds.

General Nutrition

The puréed diet should follow the 2020-2025 USDA Dietary Guidelines as closely as possible. That means it should be based on nutrient-dense whole foods and include a variety of food groups, including ample portions of fruits and vegetables.

While the goal of a puréed diet is to provide the same or similar calories and nutrition as your regular diet, research shows that puréed diets might provide fewer calories and macronutrients, including protein.

In a study from Chile that compared the nutritional value of various texture-modified diets in one hospital, researchers found a significant difference between the puréed diet and the regular house diet.2

They measured calories and macronutrients on three different days and found that meals from the puréed diet had 31% fewer calories, 45% less protein, and 41% less fat than the regular diet.

How Sustainable Is The Diet?

Acceptability of puréed foods is probably the most common complaint when it comes to the puréed diet. Some of the texture differences, especially in meats, may affect your perception of how the food tastes.

Sustaining the diet, obviously, is necessary for medical reasons. To make that easier, you can try different foods and serving methods.

• Food molds that mimic the shape of the food before it is puréed are designed to improve the acceptability. However, research shows that most people actually prefer puréed foods that are served as individual scoops rather than in molded form. See what works best for you.

• You might prefer to eat your puréed foods in the form of soups instead of solid meals. It's easy to make the adjustment—just add additional stock to the blender.

Also, keep in mind that adding extra herbs and seasonings can make a big difference in the taste of your meals.

How Flexible Is The Diet?

Any food that can be blended smooth is fair game on a puréed diet, so in that sense, there can be a world of flexibility with a puréed diet. However, that also means that you are limited in terms of what you can eat in terms of ready-prepared foods.

The best tip for making a puréed diet easier and more flexible is to plan ahead. Do as much cooking and prep work as you can ahead of time.

Prepare a few batches of fruits, vegetables, meats, and grains, and portion them out in freezer containers so all you'll have to do is thaw, heat, and puree. Likewise, you can bag smoothie ingredients and freeze them, so all you need to do is blend and go.

What equipment do I need?

Recommended basic tools

• A food processor (either size or both):

o Mini-food processor, such as the Cuisinart Mini Prep* or the KitchenAid Mini Food Processor*.

o 7 cup food processor with a good motor. You don’t need a lot of attachments.

• A powerful blender, such as the Ninja*, Vitamix or Blandtec. Choose one that is easy to clean.

• A nutrient extractor, such as the NutriBullet*, especially good for fresh fruit and vegetables.

• A fine mesh sieve to strain particles and seeds.

Tips for pureeing food

When preparing foods for a puréed diet, cook meats, vegetables, and grains until they're very soft. Moist cooking methods like simmering or braising in liquid can help add additional moisture to meats and vegetables and make them easier to purée.

Place the hardest foods (e.g., meat, chicken) in a blender or food processor along with some liquid, like milk, juice, meat, or vegetable stock and purée it until it's smooth. Next, add soft-cooked vegetables and grains as desired and purée again. You can also purée (and eat) each food separately.

All foods should be completely smooth with a consistency like pudding, very smooth mashed potatoes, or hummus. It's important that they not have any solid chunks of food or lumps if you have trouble chewing or swallowing. You can add more liquid to make them thinner, if you prefer.

When preparing your favorite soups, just be sure to blend up or strain any solid vegetables, noodles, or meat.

How to puree meat and keep the flavor

Pureeing meat can be a little tricky. Here are specific tips:

- Cook the meat. Slow cooking is best for flavor – braise, boil, slow cook, or pressure cook.
- Refrigerate for at least 2 hours.
- Chop into 1-inch pieces.
- Put a cup of meat into your food processor or blender.
- Blend the meat until it's fine and powder, almost like sand.
- Then add ½ cup of water, meat broth, or reserved cooking liquid per cup of meat.
- Safe in refrigerate for 3-4 days. Or freeze it.

• Add ¼ teaspoon salt and ½ teaspoon of spices of your choice to 1 cup of pureed meat.

Products to use to thicken pureed food

If you add too much liquid, you can thicken it up by adding more food, dried potato flakes, gelatin, flour, or a commercial thickener such as Simply Thick or ThickIt.

Ways to improve flavor

To avoid bland food, put the flavor in the sauce – not in the food as it's cooking. In other words, add herbs, spices, and flavorful sauces during the blending phase.

IDDSI points out in their FAQ for liquidized foods that people who eat an altered diet are at risk for protein-energy malnutrition and may find it hard to meet their nutritional needs.

IDDSI suggests that we don't use water as the liquid. Instead, use a compatible liquid that offers added nutrition (and more flavor) such as:

- Milk.
- Butter.
- Cream.
- Cheese.
- Gravy.
- Cream soup.
- Sour cream.

Tasty food combinations

First, use a variety of liquids when pureeing food:

- Applesauce
- Guacamole
- Salsa
- Sour cream
- Yogurt
- Butter
- Whipping cream
- Milk (dairy, soy, rice, cashew)
- Coconut milk
- Maple syrup

- Peanut butter
- Broth
- Tomato sauce
- Tomato juice (V8)
- Ensure or Boost

Second, consider these specific combinations:

- Cooked rice and butter.
- Cooked rice with coconut milk (or yogurt), frozen fruit, walnuts, and honey.
- Chicken and applesauce.
- Oatmeal with peanut butter and melted chocolate chips.
- Peanut butter & jelly sandwich and milk.
- Baked potato and beef broth.

• Ensure with banana and strawberries and canned peaches.

• Scrambled eggs with cottage cheese and milk.

• Soak banana bread in milk and then puree it.

• Baked sweet potato with butter, cinnamon, ground ginger, nutmeg, maple syrup (or brown sugar).

Sample menu for a puréed diet

Here are some examples of puréed diet options for each meal of the day. If you need help planning your meals, call the Department of Food and Nutrition to speak with a dietitian.

Meal or Snack Puréed Diet

Breakfast

- Fruit juice without pulp
- Puréed banana
- Cooked cereal with milk
- Puréed cooked egg
- Milk
- Coffee or tea

Mid-morning snack

- Vanilla or flavored yogurt

Lunch

- Any puréed or strained soup
- Puréed chicken salad
- Puréed green beans

- Puréed fruit
- Puréed rice
- Tea with sugar

Mid-afternoon snack

- Ensure plus

Dinner

- Puréed or strained soup
- Puréed meat or fish
- Mashed potato
- Puréed vegetables with olive oil or butter
- Applesauce

Evening Snack

- Vanilla Pudding

PUREED DIET RECIPES

Trying pureed-friendly recipes is a great way to explore new flavors and find new favorite dishes while looking after your health. In this part are nourishing pureed diet recipes for you to enjoy.

Carrot puree

Preparation time

30 minutes

Ingredients

• 350g carrot, peeled

Instructions

1. Chop carrots and put them in a saucepan and pour over just enough boiling water to cover.

2. Cover with a lid and simmer for 15 to 20 minutes until soft.

3. Drain the carrots and place in a blender, adding some of the water from the cooking liquid, then puree until very smooth.

Sweet potato puree

Preparation time

30 minutes

Ingredients

- 1 whole sweet potato
- 1 dash cooled boiled water or your baby's usual milk

Instructions

1. Peel the sweet potato and cut into cubes.
2. Place in a pan and cover with water.
3. Cover with a lid and simmer for 15-20 minutes, until tender.
4. Drain and puree, adding a little milk or cooled boiled water to thin to the desired consistency.

Banana and apple puree

Preparation time

18 minutes

Ingredients

- 2 whole apples, sweet
- 1 whole banana, very ripe

Instructions

1. Peel and core the apples and slice into small chunks.

2. Peel and chop the banana into small pieces.

3. Place in a pan, cover in water, bring to the boil and simmer for six to eight minutes (or until soft).

4. Drain and puree to desired consistency.

Butternut squash puree

Preparation time

55 minutes

Ingredients

- 1 whole butternut squash
- 2 tbsp olive oil
- 1 dash cooled boiled water or your baby's usual milk

Instructions

1. Cut the butternut squash in half lengthways, and scoop out the seeds.
2. Use a sharp knife to score a criss-cross pattern in the flesh.
3. Place the squash skin-side down on a baking sheet.

4. Drizzle olive oil over each half and then wrap in foil.

5. Cook in the oven at 180C for 45 minutes.

6. Remove and leave to cool.

7. Scoop the flesh into a bowl and blend to the desired consistency, adding a little cooled boiled water or your baby's usual milk to thin it, if required.

Courgette, pea and kale puree

Preparation time

18 minutes

Ingredients

- 200g peas, fresh or frozen
- 1 medium courgette
- 200g kale, fresh

Instructions

1. Wash the courgette and cut into small chunks.
2. Wash the kale and remove any tough stalks.
3. Place all the ingredients in a large pan and cover with boiling water.
4. Return to the boil, then simmer for 6 to 8 minutes, until the kale is cooked and the courgette is tender.
5. Drain and puree to the required consistency.

Sweet potato and basil puree

Preparation time

25 minutes

Ingredients

- 4 medium sweet potatoes
- 5 whole basil leaves
- 1 tbsp olive oil, optional

Instructions

1. Scrub and peel 3 – 4 sweet potatoes and cut into even-sized chunks.

2. Place in a saucepan and cover with boiling water.

3. Bring to the boil, then reduce the heat and simmer for approximately 15 minutes, until tender.

4. Drain the potatoes and place in a blender.

5. Add the basil leaves and puree to the desired consistency, adding a little olive oil to thin if necessary.

Sweet potato and pear puree

Preparation time

45 minutes

Ingredients

- 3 large sweet potatoes
- 4 whole conference pears

Instructions

1. Scrub and peel the sweet potatoes, then chop into 2cm cubes.
2. Place sweet potatoes in a pan and cover with boiling water.
3. Bring back to the boil and simmer for around 15 minutes, until just tender.
4. Meanwhile, peel and chop the pears.

5. Add the chopped pears to the pan and return to the boil for around six minutes.

6. Drain and mash or puree, as required.

Pear and rice puree

Preparation time

20 minutes

Ingredients

- Conference pears 10
- Baby rice 1tbsp

Instructions

1. Peel and core 8 – 10 pears and chop into 2cm cubes.

2. Place in a pan and cover with boiling water.

3. Bring back to the boil then reduce the heat and simmer for around 5 minutes, until tender.

4. Drain and puree to the desired consistency, stirring in the baby rice.

Avocado and mint puree

Preparation time

14 minutes

Ingredients

- 1 whole avocado, large and ripe
- 6 whole mint leaf

Instructions

1. Slice the avocado in half lengthways, and twist to separate the 2 halves.

2. Carefully remove the stone with the tip of a knife.

3. Scoop the avocado flesh from the skin using a dessert spoon.

4. Place in a bowl and mash with a fork or potato masher.

5. Finely chop the mint and mix into the mashed avocado.

6. For newly weaned babies, puree until smooth if preferred.

Annabel Karmel's blueberry, pear and banana puree

Preparation time

10 minutes

Ingredients

- 2 pears, peeled and diced
- 150g blueberries

- 1 banana, sliced

Instructions

1. Put the pears and blueberries into a saucepan.

2. Simmer for 5 minutes until soft

3. Add the banana and blend until smooth.

Spiced apple puree

Preparation time

28 minutes

Ingredients

- 8 whole apples, ripe
- 1 pinch nutmeg, dried
- 1 pinch cinnamon, dried

Instructions

1. Peel and core 6 – 8 of the apples, and chop into small, even chunks.

2. Place in a pan, cover with water and bring to the boil.

3. Simmer for 6 to 8 minutes, until soft.

4. Drain and puree to the desired consistency, adding the spices.

Spinach and roasted carrot puree

Preparation time

40 Minutes

Ingredients

- Medium carrot 2 whole, peeled
- Fresh Spinach 2 large handfuls, washedIngredients

Instructions

1. Cut the carrots into sticks or slices, and wrap with the spinach in a foil parcel.

2. Place on a baking tray and bake at 190C/375F/Gas mark 5 for around half an hour, or until the carrots are tender.

3. Blend to the required consistency, adding a little breastmilk, formula or cooled boiled water if necessary.

Orchard fruit puree

Preparation time

10 minutes

Ingredients

- 1 whole medium eating apple
- 10 whole cherries
- 1 whole peach

Instructions

1. Peel and chop the apple.
2. Place in a saucepan and cover with boiling water.
3. Cook for a few minutes on a low heat until the apple has softened.
4. Stone and chop the cherries.
5. Peel and chop the peach into chunks.

6. Strain the apple and add to the cherries and peaches then blend to the correct consistency: runny for newly weaning babies; lumpier for older babies.

Annabel Karmel's Salmon surprise puree

Preparation time

25 minutes

Ingredients

- 200g carrots, peeled and sliced
- 125g salmon fillet, skinned
- 60ml orange juice

- 40g grated Cheddar cheese
- 15g unsalted butter
- 2 tbsp milk

Instructions

1. Put the carrots into a saucepan, cover with water, bring to the boil and cook over a medium heat for about 20 minutes until tender.

2. Alternatively, place the vegetables in a steamer and cook for 20 minutes.

3. Meanwhile, place the salmon in a suitable dish, pour over the orange juice and scatter over the cheese.

4. Cover, leaving an air vent and microwave on high for about 2 minutes or until the fish flakes easily with a fork.

5. Alternatively, cover with foil and cook in a 180°C/ 350°F/Gas 4 pre-heated oven for about 20 minutes.

6. Flake the fish with a fork, carefully removing any bones.

7. Drain the carrots, mix with the butter and milk and puree in a blender together with the flaked fish and its sauce.

8. For older babies, mash the carrots together with the butter and the milk and then mix the flaked fish with the mashed carrots.

Annabel Karmel's peach, apple and strawberry puree

Preparation time

20 minutes

Ingredients

- 1 apple, peeled, cored and chopped
- 2tbsp apple juice or water
- 115g ripe strawberries, hulled
- 1 ripe peach, skinned, stoned and sliced
- 1tbsp baby rice

Instructions

1. Put the chopped apple into a saucepan with 2tbsp apple juice or water.

2. Cover and simmer for 5 minutes.

3. Add the strawberries and sliced peach and cook for 2 to 3 minutes.

4. Blend until smooth and stir in the baby rice.

Annabel Karmel's potato, carrot and sweetcorn puree

Preparation time

26 minutes

Ingredients

- 25g unsalted butter
- 50g onion, peeled and chopped
- 175g carrots, peeled and chopped
- 200g potatoes, peeled and chopped
- 250ml vegetable stock or water
- 50g tinned or frozen sweetcorn
- 1-2tbsp milk

Instructions

1. Melt the butter in a pan and sauté the onion for 1 minute.

2. Add the carrots and sauté for 5 minutes.

3. Tip in the potatoes, cover with the stock or water and cook over a medium heat for 15 minutes.

4. Add the sweetcorn and continue to cook for 5 minutes.

5. Purée the mixture through a mouli and stir in the milk to make it the right consistency for your baby.

Butternut squash and apricot puree

Preparation time

10 minutes

Ingredients

- 200g butternut squash
- 50g dried apricot

Instructions

1. Peel and chop the butternut squash.
2. Place in a saucepan.
3. Cover with boiling water and cook on a medium heat until tender (around 15 minutes).

4. Chop the apricots into small pieces.

5. Drain the butternut squash and add to the apricots.

6. Blend until you reach the desired consistency.

Annabel Karmel's apricot, apple and pear puree with vanilla

Preparation time

13 minutes

Ingredients

- 75g ready-to-eat dried apricots, chopped
- 1 large apple, peeled, cored and chopped
- 1 vanilla pod
- 4tbsp apple juice or water
- 1 large ripe pear, peeled, cored and chopped

Instructions

1. Put the apricots and apple into a heavy-based saucepan together with the apple juice or water.

2. Scrape the vanilla pod seeds into the pan and throw in the split pod.

3. Bring to the boil, then cover and simmer for 3 to 4 minutes.

4. Add the chopped pear and continue to simmer for 2 minutes.

Blueberry, apple and peach puree

Preparation time

20 minutes

Ingredients

- 3 whole sweet eating apple, peeled, cored and finely chopped
- 2 whole ripe peaches, peeled and chopped
- 50g blueberries
- 4 tbsp water

- 1 tbsp baby rice, (optional)

Instructions

1. Put the fruit into a heavy based, lidded saucepan with the water and cook over a low heat taking care that it doesn’t burn.

2. Add a little more water if necessary.

3. When the apples are soft, puree in a blender untll you reach the desired consistency for your baby’s age (smooth for first foods).

4. If the mixture is too thin, stir in a tablespoon of baby rice to thicken and add texture.

Apple, pear and apricot puree

Preparation time

16 Minutes

Ingredients

- 4 tbsp water
- 1 whole eating apple, peeled and chopped
- 750g dried, stoned apricots, chopped into small pieces
- 1 whole ripe pear, peeled and chopped

Instructions

1. Add the water to a large saucepan and add the apple and apricots.

2. Bring to the boil and simmer for 3 or 4 minutes.

3. Stir in the chopped pear and simmer for a couple more minutes.

4. Wait to cool and puree in a blender.

5. Stir fruit purees into plain yoghurt for a delicious healthy pudding for babies or grown-ups.

Sweet potato and lentil puree

Preparation time

55 minutes

Ingredients

- 1 large knob unsalted butter
- 1 whole large carrot, peeled and chopped into small pieces
- 60g red lentils
- 200g sweet potato, peeled and chopped into chunks
- 1 whole bay leaf
- 475ml very low salt vegetable stock or water

Instructions

1. Melt the butter in a saucepan.

2. Stir the carrots and lentils into the butter, and cook for two minutes.

3. Add the sweet potato, bay leaf and stock or water.

4. Bring to the boil, then simmer for 30 minutes or until the lentils and vegetables are soft.

5. Remove the bay leaf, then blend into a puree, or mash for older babies.

Cheesy carrot, parsnip and potato puree

Preparation time

40 Minutes

Ingredients

- 2 large carrots
- 1 medium parsnip
- 1 medium potato
- 25g cheddar cheese, grated

Instructions

1. Peel and chop all of the vegetables.
2. Place in a pan and cover with water.
3. Bring to the boil and simmer for 20 minutes or until tender.
4. Drain, reserving a little cooking water.
5. Add the grated cheese.

6. Puree the vegetables and cheese until smooth, adding up to 2 tablespoons of the cooking water to thin.

Courgette and cauliflower puree

Preparation time

30 Minutes

Ingredients

- 200g courgette
- 100g cauliflower floret (fresh or frozen)

Instructions

1. Cook the cauliflower florets in boiling water for 10-12 minutes until soft (or according to packet instructions, if using frozen cauliflower).

2. Drain and set aside.

3. Peel and chop the courgette, then steam until tender (around 8 minutes).

4. Combine the vegetables and blend to desired consistency.

Parsnip and pea puree

Preparation time

30 Minutes

Ingredients

- 100g frozen peas
- 1 whole medium parsnip

Instruction

1. Peel the parsnip, cut into chunks and boil for 10-15 minutes, until soft.

2. Add the peas, bring back to the boil and cook for a further 5 minutes.

3. Drain, reserving some of the cooking water, and blend to the required consistency, adding some of the reserved water if necessary.

Pear and swede puree

Preparation time

45 Minutes

Ingredients

- 1 whole small swede
- 2 whole medium pear

Instructions

1. Peel swede, cut into chunks and boil for 15 minutes until soft.

2. Peel, core and chop the pears.

3. Add to the pan and cook for a further 5 to 10 minutes.

4. Drain and blend until smooth.

Butternut squash and carroty mash with thyme

Preparation time

1 Hour 20 Minutes

Ingredients

- 200g butternut squash, swede or pumpkin
- 1 whole medium carrot
- 4 whole new potato

- 1 tsp fresh thyme, chopped
- 1 dash olive oil

Instructions

1. Peel the squash, swede or pumpkin and cut into thick slices.
2. Place in a roasting tin and drizzle with olive oil.
3. Roast at 200C/400F/Gas mark 6 for 30-40 minutes, or until soft.
4. Prepare the carrots and potatoes and boil until soft.
5. Add the thyme to the cooked vegetables and blend to a smooth puree.

Butternut squash and banana puree

Prepartion time

1 hour 10 minutes

Ingredients

- 1 whole butternut squash
- 1 whole ripe banana

Instructions

1. Prick the whole butternut squash all over with a fork, wrap in foil and place on a baking tray. Bake in the oven at 180C/350F/Gas mark 4, for 1 hour.

2. Remove the squash from the oven and leave to cool.

3. Cut in half, scrape out the seeds and scoop out the flesh.

4. Place the flesh in a bowl with the chopped banana and mash together.

Avocado and pear puree

Prepartion time

10 Minutes

Ingredients

- 1 whole medium avocado
- 100g fresh pears or tinned in juice

Instructions

1. If using fresh pears, peel, chop and place in a saucepan.

2. Cover with boiling water.

3. Cook on a low heat until softened.

4. If using tinned pears, drain well.

5. Cut the avocado in half and remove the stone.

6. Scoop out the flesh and chop roughly.

7. Drain the pear and add to the avocado.

8. Blend until you reach the required consistency.

Summer berry puree

Prepartion time

10 Minutes

Ingredients

- 100g blueberry (fresh or frozen)
- 100g strawberry (fresh, frozen or tinned)
- 100g raspberry (fresh, frozen or tinned)

Instructions

1. Prepare the fruit. Wash and remove any stalks from fresh berries, drain tinned berries and

defrost frozen berries according to the instructions on the packet.

2. Combine the berries and blend until you reach the required consistency.

3. Pass the mixture through a fine sieve with a wooden spoon if you want to remove the small seeds.

Tropical fruit puree

Prepartion time

10 Minutes

Ingredients

- 200g mango
- 200g papaya
- 1 whole large banana

Instructions

1. Peel and chop the mango into chunks.
2. Peel and chop the banana.
3. Peel the papaya and scoop out the fruit, making sure you have removed all the seeds.
4. Place the ingredients in a container and blend to the required consistency.

10 NO-COOK HOMEMADE BABY FOOD

Prepartion time

5 minutes

INGREDIENTS

- 1 cup blueberries
- diced strawberries
- diced peaches (peeled)
- diced kiwi (peeled)
- diced pineapple (peeled)
- diced banana (peeled)
- diced mango (peeled)

- diced avocado (peeled), or beans (rinsed and drained)
- water

INSTRUCTIONS

1. Choose one fruit, the avocado, or beans and add to a blender.

2. If making the puree with blueberries, strawberries, peaches, kiwi, pineapple, mango, or beans.

3. Add 1/4 cup water and blend, adding more water as desired to make a thin, very smooth puree.

4. If making avocado or banana, just blend (without water) until very smooth.

5. Serve or store in an airtight container for 3-5 days in the fridge, or up to 3 months in the freezer.

Sweet Puréed Carrots With Orange and Ginger

Preparation time

30 minutes

Ingredients

- 2 pounds carrots, peeled and cut into ½ inch slices
- 2 cups vegetable broth
- 1 tablespoon sugar

- 1/2 teaspoon kosher salt, plus more to taste
- 1/4 cup olive oil
- 1 tablespoon fresh ginger, peeled and finely grated
- 2 cloves of garlic, minced
- 1/3 cup fresh orange juice
- Freshly ground pepper, to taste

Instructions

1. In a large saucepan, set over medium heat, combine carrots, broth, sugar, and salt.
2. Bring to a simmer, cover, and cook for 20 minutes, until the carrots are very tender.

3. Drain the carrots, reserving ¼ cup of the cooking liquid.

4. In a medium saucepan set over medium-low heat, warm up the olive oil.

5. Add the garlic and ginger, and cook, stirring frequently, until softened and fragrant, about 2-3 minutes.

6. Remove from the heat.

7. Add everything to a food processor and purée until smooth, scraping down the sides to make sure everything is combined.

8. For a smoother purée, add 2 tablespoons of the reserved cooking liquid.

9. Season with salt and pepper.

10. Serve immediately.

Pumpkin Pie Spice Bourbon Cocktail

Preparation time

3 minutes

Ingredients

- 1/4 cup bourbon
- 1/4 cup simple syrup
- 2 tablespoons pumpkin puree
- 1/2 teaspoon McCormick Pure Pumpkin Pie Spice Blend Extract

Instructions

1. Mix all ingredients until well blended.

2. Pour into an ice-filled beverage glass.

3. Serve immediately.

Pumpkin Pie Spice White Russian

Prepartion time

3 minutes

Ingredients

- 2 tablespoons heavy cream
- 1/2 teaspoon McCormick Pure Pumpkin Pie Spice Blend Extract
- 1/4 cup coffee liqueur

- 2 tablespoons vodka

Instructions

1. Mix heavy cream and extract.

2. Add coffee liqueur and vodka to ice-filled beverage glass; stir gently.

3. Pour cream mixture over the top.

4. Serve immediately.

Slow Cooker Chicken Noodle Soup

Preparation time

4 hours 30 minutes

Ingredients

- 1 package of McCormick® Slow Cookers Chicken Noodle Soup Recipe & Seasoning Mix
- 1 pound boneless skinless chicken breasts, cut into 3/4-inch cubes
- 2 cups sliced carrots
- 1 cup sliced celery
- 1 cup chopped onion
- 4 cups water
- 1 cup uncooked medium egg noodles

Instructions

1. Place chicken and vegetables in slow cooker.

2. Mix Seasoning and water in bowl until blended.

3. Pour over chicken and vegetables and stir to coat.

4. Replace ccover on slow cooker.

5. Cook 8 hours on LOW or 4 hours on HIGH.

6. Stir in noodles.

7. Cover. Cook 10 minutes longer on HIGH or until noodles are tender.

Slow Cooker Chicken Tortilla Soup

Prepartion time

4 hours 15 minutes

Ingredients

- 1 package of slow cookers limited edition chicken tortilla soup seasoning
- 1 1/2 pound boneless skinless chicken breasts, cut into 1/2-inch cubes
- 2 cups frozen chopped bell pepper and onion blend
- 4 cups Kitchen Basics® All Natural Original Chicken Stock

- 1 can of petite diced tomatoes, undrained
- 1 cup crushed tortilla chips

Instructions

1. Place chicken and frozen vegetables in slow cooker.
2. Mix Seasoning Mix, stock and tomatoes in bowl until blended.
3. Pour mixture over chicken and vegetables and stir to coat.
4. Cover slow cooker.
5. Cook 8 hours on LOW or 4 hours on HIGH.
6. Ladle into soup bowls.
7. Sprinkle with tortilla chips.

8. Serve with desired toppings, such as chopped avocado, shredded cheese, chopped green onions, chopped cilantro, sour cream, or lime wedges.

Made in the USA
Columbia, SC
23 October 2022